Written by: *Ron Marz & David A. Rodriguez*
Art by: *Fico Ossio*
Colors by: *Ander Zarate*
Letters by: AW's *Deron Bennett & DC Hopkins*

HC ISBN: 978-1-63140-412-2 | TPB ISBN: 978-1-63140-430-6

18 17 16 15   1 2 3 4

IDW
www.IDWPUBLISHING.com
IDW founded by Ted Adams, Alex Garner,
Kris Oprisko, and Robbie Robbins

Ted Adams, CEO & Publisher
Greg Goldstein, President & COO
Robbie Robbins, EVP/Sr. Graphic Artist
Chris Ryall, Chief Creative Officer/Editor-in-Chief
Matthew Ruzicka, CPA, Chief Financial Officer
Alan Payne, VP of Sales
Dirk Wood, VP of Marketing
Lorelei Bunjes, VP of Digital Services
Jeff Webber, VP of Digital Publishing & Business Development

Facebook: **facebook.com/idwpublishing**
Twitter: **@idwpublishing**
YouTube: **youtube.com/idwpublishing**
Tumblr: **tumblr.idwpublishing.com**
Instagram: **instagram.com/idwpublishing**

RIFT INTO OVERDRIVE

EVER SINCE THOSE RIDICULOUS *TRAP LOSERS* LOCKED ME UP, I'VE SOMEHOW GROWN STRONGER AND STRONGER.

IT WASN'T LONG BEFORE I WAS ABLE TO LEAVE MY CELL FOR SHORT PERIODS OF TIME, WITHOUT THEM EVEN *KNOWING.*

I SEARCHED FOR *WEAKNESS,* AND DETERMINED THE *EXACT* ORDER OF EVENTS NEEDED TO EXECUTE A *GRAND PLAN* THAT WILL *CRUSH* THE SKYLANDERS ONCE AND FOR ALL!

OH, NOT *AGAIN.* DON'T YOU THINK YOU SHOULD *RECONSIDER?* MAYBE TAKE SOME TIME OFF?

NONSENSE! SOMETHING IN THIS ACADEMY HAS BEEN *FEEDING* MY POWER, MAKING ME THE *MIGHTIEST* PORTAL MASTER EVER!

AND AFTER MONTHS OF *SEARCHING* THIS CURSED SCHOOL...

...I HAVE *FOUND* IT!

LATER...

LISTEN UP, EVERYONE. I KNOW YOU'RE ALL *WORRIED* RIGHT NOW, AND I'D BE LYING IF I SAID YOU SHOULD FEEL OTHERWISE.

WHAT WE'RE FACING NOW IS AN *EVIL* GREATER THAN WE'VE EVER KNOWN. AND FOR US, THAT'S SAYING A *LOT*.

THE *PORTALS* ARE DOWN, NOT JUST THE ONES AT THE ACADEMY, BUT THE ENTIRE *NETWORK*. THAT MEANS THE *REST* OF THE SKYLANDERS ARE STRANDED WHEREVER THEY ARE...

...AND WE CAN'T EVEN *CONTACT* ANYONE TO LET THEM KNOW WE'RE IN TROUBLE.

SO IT'S UP TO OUR SMALL GROUP TO FIGURE OUT WHAT'S *CAUSING* THESE TERRIBLE RIFTS, AND THEN *STOP* KAOS AND HIS NEW ARMY.

SPYRO, HOW ARE WE SUPPOSED TO *FIGHT* THOSE ELITE DROW, AND WHATEVER ELSE KAOS HAS IN HIS ARSENAL, WHEN WE CAN'T USE AIRSHIPS *OR* PORTALS TO GET WHERE WE NEED TO GO?

THAT'S A FINE QUESTION, GILL. FORTUNATELY FOR US, THERE'S A WAY THAT EVEN KAOS DOESN'T KNOW ABOUT.

BEFORE THERE WERE PORTALS, THE BENEVOLENT ANCIENTS USED POWERFUL ARTIFACTS CALLED *RIFT ENGINES*...

...*EXPLORING* THE COUNTLESS WORLDS OF THE UNIVERSE AND *CONNECTING* THEM WITHIN THE VAST NETWORK OF PORTALS.

IF WE CAN SOMEHOW *RECOVER* THOSE RIFT ENGINES, IT'S POSSIBLE THAT MAGS AND SHARPFIN COULD DEVISE A WAY TO *REPURPOSE* THEM FOR TRAVEL THROUGHOUT SKYLANDS...

...AND POSSIBLY *BEYOND*.

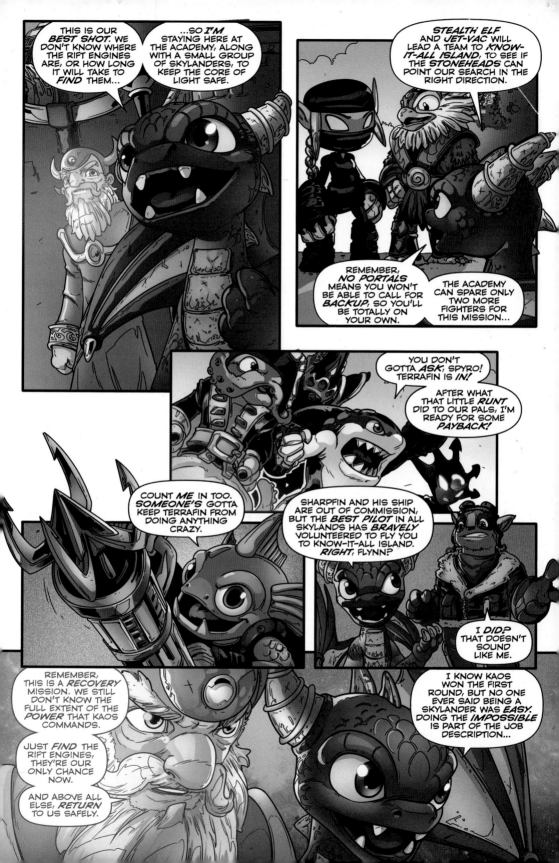

"...SO NOW IT'S TIME TO GO TO *WORK!*"

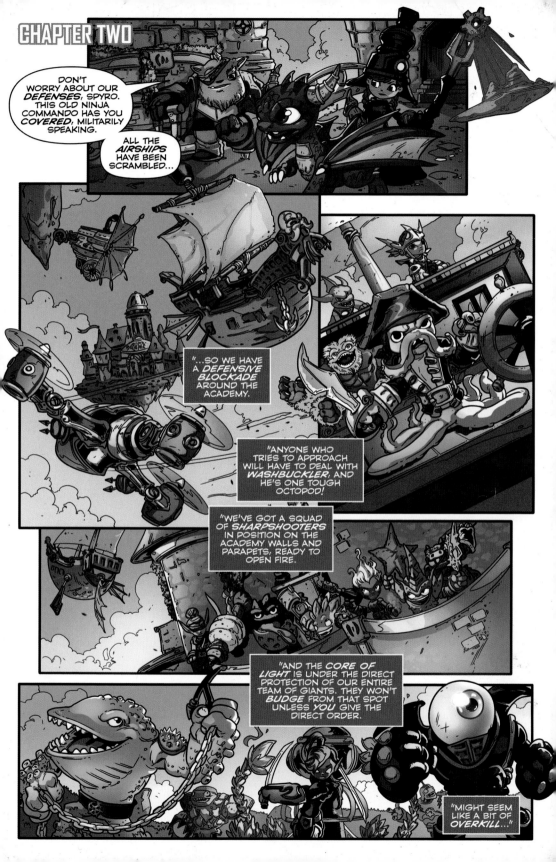

CHAPTER TWO

DON'T WORRY ABOUT OUR *DEFENSES*, SPYRO. THIS OLD NINJA COMMANDO HAS YOU *COVERED*, MILITARILY SPEAKING.

ALL THE *AIRSHIPS* HAVE BEEN SCRAMBLED...

"...SO WE HAVE A *DEFENSIVE BLOCKADE* AROUND THE ACADEMY.

"ANYONE WHO TRIES TO APPROACH WILL HAVE TO DEAL WITH *WASHBUCKLER*, AND HE'S ONE TOUGH OCTOPOD!

"WE'VE GOT A SQUAD OF *SHARPSHOOTERS* IN POSITION ON THE ACADEMY WALLS AND PARAPETS, READY TO OPEN FIRE.

"AND THE *CORE OF LIGHT* IS UNDER THE DIRECT PROTECTION OF OUR ENTIRE TEAM OF GIANTS. THEY WON'T *BUDGE* FROM THAT SPOT UNLESS *YOU* GIVE THE DIRECT ORDER.

"MIGHT SEEM LIKE A BIT OF *OVERKILL...*"

"...I HOPE THINGS ARE GOING BETTER BACK AT THE *ACADEMY*."

YOU KNOW, WE'VE SEEN A *LOT* OF ACTION TOGETHER, REX. THE ARKEYANS, THE DOOM RAIDERS, MALEFOR. AND NO MATTER THE ODDS, WE ALWAYS *WON*.

BUT THESE *SKY RIFTS* HAVE ME SHAKING IN MY SPOKES.

THERE'S NO SHAME IN *FEAR*, BOUNCER. *EVERYBODY* HERE IS FEELING IT.

BUT WE ARE THE *GIANTS*, THE *FIRST* SKYLANDERS.

WHEN OTHERS NEED *COURAGE*, THEY WILL LOOK TO US. NOT BECAUSE WE ARE THE *BIGGEST*, OR THE *STRONGEST*...

...BUT BECAUSE EVEN THOUGH WE'RE *AFRAID*, WE KEEP *FIGHTING*.

WE'LL DO *OUR* JOBS...

"...AND TRUST EON AND THE OTHER BIG BRAINS TO FIND THE *ANSWER* TO THESE RIFTS."

THE UPSIDE IS THE RIFTS ARE SO *DESTRUCTIVE*, IT'S EASY TO DETECT THEIR ENERGY FLUXES.

THE DOWNSIDE IS THERE'S SO *MANY* OF 'EM, I CAN BARELY KEEP TRACK!

THE RIFTS ARE APPEARING IN EVER-WIDENING CONCENTRIC CIRCLES. THAT MEANS THERE'S *NO WAY* THERE'S A NATURAL OCCURRENCE.

SOMETHING'S *SYSTEMATICALLY* CHOMPING UP THE SKY! AND EACH RIFT IS DRAINING OFF SOME OF THE *MAGIC* THAT MAKES OUR WORLD SPECIAL.

IF WE DON'T STOP THIS *SOON*, MAGS...

...IT WILL MEAN THE *END* OF SKYLANDS FOREVER.

HOPE YOU DON'T MIND ME TAKING THE WHEEL THERE, OLD TIMER.

BUT I THOUGHT YOU MIGHT WANT TO SEE HOW THE *BEST PILOT* IN SKYLANDS DOES THINGS.

CHAPTER THREE

DIDN'T *YOUR* SHIP JUST GET DESTROYED IN A RIFT?

IF YOU MEAN I *SACRIFICED* MY NOBLE VESSEL IN THE NAME OF THE GREATER GOOD, THEN YES, I *DID*, MY MUSTACHIOED MABU FRIEND.

BUT THAT'S JUST ANOTHER DAY IN THE LIFE OF A *HEROIC ADVENTURER* LIKE MYSELF.

THAT'S *AMAZING!* TELL ME *MORE*, FLYNN!

WHY, SURE THING, BLOBBERS. ANYTHING FOR A *FAN*.

ALLOW ME TO PAINT A *WORD PICTURE* FOR YOU. *THERE* I WAS, FACING OFF AGAINST A STINGING SWARM OF CORN HORNETS...

...AND ALL I HAD WITH ME WAS MY BEST RED SCARF, TWELVE GALLONS OF GUACAMOLE, AND THESE TWO FISTS OF *AWESOMENESS*.

THEY WERE *OUTGUNNED*, AND THEY *KNEW* IT. SO I TOTALLY LOWERED THE...

...BOOM?

THE OMNI-DISRUPTOR!

WHAT'S *THAT*?

CALI'S *RIGHT!* REMEMBER WHEN BLADES AND BOUNCER FOUGHT *MACHINE MAGUS* A WHILE BACK?

SURE, THAT *OMNI-DISRUPTOR* HE BUILT *BLOCKED* PORTAL ACCESS ON A LOCAL LEVEL.

BUT IF SOMEONE WITH *MORE RESOURCES* GOT HOLD OF THOSE PLANS...

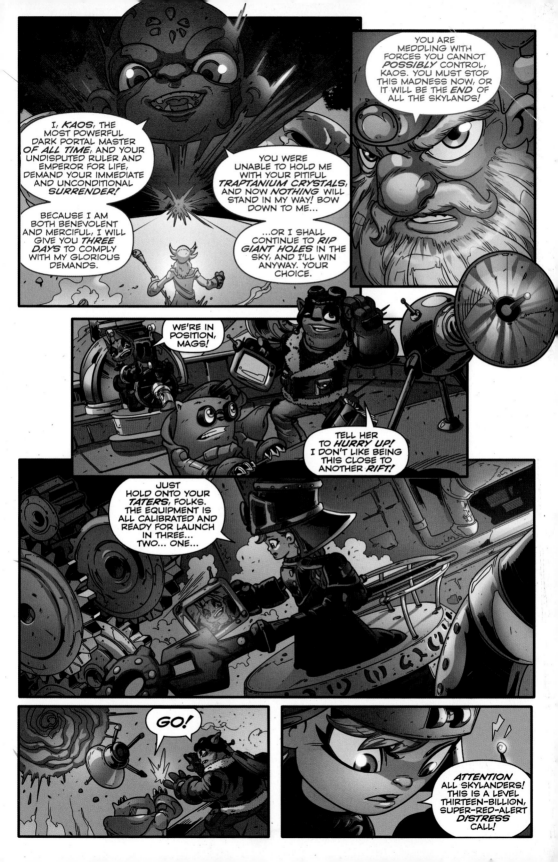

SPITFIRE

BIO

Spitfire was on pace to become the fastest driver in the Super Skylands Racing Circuit. With his lightning-quick reflexes and nerves of steel, this tech-enhanced flame spirit was absolutely unbeatable. But during the championship event at Skywinder Canyon, he was illegally bumped off course by a goblin racer and sent flying into the canyon wall in a fiery explosion! Most thought that this would put an end to his racing career. But three weeks later, he was back on the track, more fired up than ever to claim the title. Unfortunately, it was then that all of Skylands fell under the rule of Kaos in his Sky Eating machine, and the racing came to an end. That's when Spitfire was approached by Master Eon with an offer that could get him back behind the wheel as the new leader of an elite driving team— the Skylander SuperChargers!

STORMBLADE

BIO

From the moment she left the nest, *Stormblade* had always pushed the boundaries, seeking to travel further than anyone had ever gone. At a young age, she made the bold leap off of her home island and plummeted through the deep blue sky in an attempt to find the bottom of Skylands—only to find no such bottom existed. This did not fulfill her curiosity, nor did it sway her belief there was something else beyond the limits of her world. Soon she built a custom ship, the Sky Slicer, and raced to the furthest reaches of Skylands in search of its end—but no end could be found. She wanted answers, and so she came to the one person who could help her—Master Eon. The Portal Master instantly saw the unquenchable thirst for exploration that resided in Stormblade, and asked her to join the Skylanders on a very special mission that would take her through the uncharted rifts between worlds!

FIESTA

BIO

Despite being undead, *Fiesta* had always been the life of the party. He was once the head member of a popular mariachi band in the personal court of Count Moneybone, who all undead citizens respected immensely. In his spare time, Fiesta and his bandmates played music for all of the new arrivals that entered the Underworld. However, a day came when the new arrivals were actually several Skylanders, who had come on a mission to stop Count Moneybone from unleashing a robot army on all of Skylands. Fiesta then realized that he, like so many others, had been fooled by the evil count into thinking the count was kind and generous—not the vengeful monster he truly was. Unbeknownst to the Skylanders, Fiesta and his bandmates helped to distract the robot army so they could infiltrate Moneybone's mansion and put a stop to him. Even though the Skylanders were unaware, this act of bravery and defiance did catch the attention of Master Eon, who recruited him at once.

SMASH HIT

BIO

Smash Hit came from a long line of Warsupials—a rare species widely renowned for their skills in combat. But in more peaceful times, his people were responsible for locating and demolishing any remaining artifacts from the Arkeyan Empire that were deemed too dangerous to leave standing. Smash Hit liked his job because it allowed him to do what he loved most—break things! He was so skillful with his wrecking ball that he could single-handedly dismantle an entire Arkeyan Conquertron in under an hour and still have time for a snack. When Master Eon noticed his skill, he enlisted the talented Warsupial into a new wrecking crew he was forming to take on Kaos—the SuperChargers!

DIVE-CLOPS

BIO

Believe it or not, *Dive-Clops* is actually the twin brother of Eye-Brawl. When he was young, his batwings were blasted off by pirates while flying over the Swirling Sea, causing him to plunge into the abyss below. After rolling on the bottom for several days, he was discovered by an underwater civilization of Jelly Dwarves. They were instantly fascinated by the bizarre-looking eyeball and took him back to their Corral Castle, where they built him a magnificent dive suit that would allow him to explore the depths of the sea. But everything changed when Dive-Clops decided to venture to the mysterious Whirlpool of Destiny deep within the ocean. As he got closer, he suddenly felt pulled by its immense power, and reemerged to discover that thousands of years had passed! Now with his destiny before him as a member of the Skylanders, Dive-Clops lets the minions of Kaos know that there are many dangers of the deep!

HIGH VOLT

BIO

High Volt was once the commander of a special security force that was in charge of patrolling the border between the known regions of Skylands and the mysterious uncharted region known as the Outlands. From atop the Shockspire Tower, their security headquarters, High Volt vigilantly monitored any strange activity beyond the border, knowing that Kaos and his minions were always up to no good. Over the years, he had defended Skylands against countless Greeble attacks, Troll uprisings, and even a few evil food chains that were attempting to expand. But on a recent patrol mission into the Outlands, High Volt discovered a heavily guarded construction site, where Kaos' minions appeared to be building a colossal Doom Station of Ultimate Destruction! Realizing at once that all of Skylands was in danger, he raced to the Skylanders Academy to inform Master Eon and joined the Skylanders in their fight to stop it!

SPLAT

BIO

Splat grew up in a typical faun village, which was perfectly manicured and orderly. Every day in school, she and her classmates would recite the same poems, play the same music, and paint the same picture—which was always a portrait of their great ancestor, Fluty Hoofdancer. But this didn't suit Splat. The only art she wanted to learn was the art of war! After school, she would sneak off to the river and practice her own free-form fighting technique against Chompies and other creatures that were causing trouble. When the elder fauns learned of this, they were outraged. But soon thereafter, a band of Drow attacked the village to steal their valuable art, and while the other fauns cowered in fear, Splat stood her ground. Unleashing her self-taught fighting style, she defended her village and sent the Drow running. Now, as a member of the Skylanders, Splat makes quite the impression wherever she goes!

THRILLIPEDE

BIO

Thrillipede served in the Millipede Military in the outer regions of Skylands. As the top pilot in his unit, Thrillipede was responsible for single-handedly blasting over 300 Greeble warships out of the sky! When the Great Greeble War came to an end, he returned to his hometown of Flutter Bay as a celebrated hero. He was the talk of the town and everyone wanted to shake the many hands of the famous young pilot. News of his heroics eventually made their way to Captain Flynn at the Skylander Academy, who set out to determine if the stories were true. In a series of friendly challenges, the two pilots raced, soared through obstacles, and performed incredible stunts in front of a cheering Flutter Bay crowd. In each event, Thrillipede stood victorious, and was asked to join the Skylanders shortly after. Of course, Flynn later admitted that he "let him win" so that Thrillipede wouldn't be embarrassed in front of his hometown.

5